Richard Scarry's
First Little Learners

Shapes and
Opposites

SHASPES

This is a triangle.

A pennant has the shape of a triangle.

This is a square.

A checkerboard has the shape of a square.

This is a circle.

A full moon has the shape of a circle...

... so do buttons!

6

This is a rectangle.

This is, too!

Books have the shape of a rectangle.

This is a diamond.

Kites are diamond-shaped.

This shape is a star.

Good for you, Freddie!

LINES

This line is curved.

This line is straight.

Jump ropes have curved lines.

A ruler has a straight line.

Spaghetti noodles have squiggly lines.

Willy is drawing a zig-zag line.

crossed lines

Some lines are thin...

... others are thick.

Lines that go the same direction
are parallel lines.

Lined paper
has parallel lines.

A line of dashes is a broken line.

Mr. Paint Pig paints a broken line
on the street.

A line of dots is a dotted line.

(You can write your name on this dotted line.)

9

WHICH WAY?

above

between

The airplane flies above the boat.

The submarine goes under the boat.

below

Dad is ahead.

Son is behind him.

right-side up

upside-down

Tommy pulls to the left.

Timmy pulls to the right.

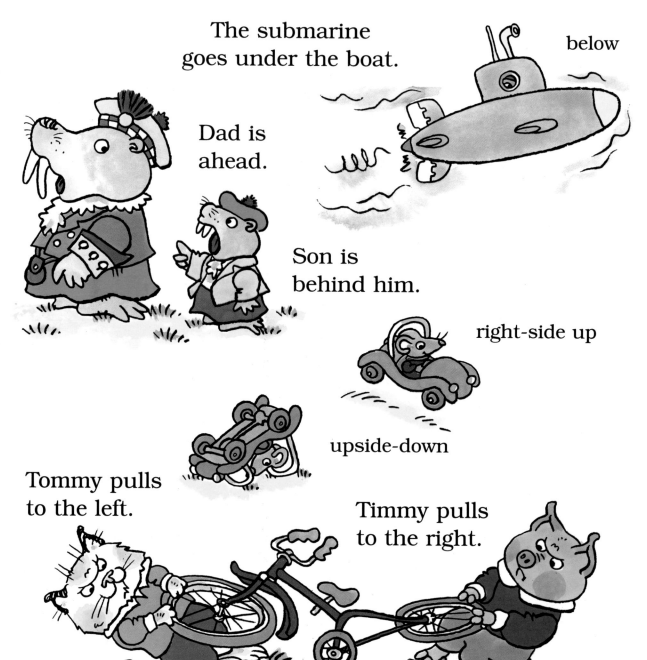

going over

going around

going under

Arthur has placed
his lunchbox beside him.
He sits beside it.

Mr. Frumble drives
backward.

Mr. Frumble
drives forward.

My, he doesn't drive very well, does he?

11

HIGH AND LOW

This bug
is high up.

This plane
is going
up.

This bug
is low down.

This plane
is going
down.

at the
top

at the
bottom

This bear
is down.

This bear
is up.

12

The mouse is small.

BIG AND SMALL

The elephant is big.

This piggy is fat.

Lowly is thin.

Hilda is heavy.

Dandelion seeds are light.

13

AMOUNTS

The bakers have lots of cupcakes.

Lowly eats one.

Thank you, bakers!

The children's breakfast bowls are full.

When they have finished eating, the bowls are empty.

They bring their bowls back to the kitchen. Aren't they helpful!

A bus carries many people.

A pencil car carries just a couple.

Hilda is eating all the cookies.

Lowly has none.

Hey! You should share!

OPPOSITES

front   back

good boys

bad boys

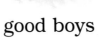

16

Mr. Rabbit stays dry.

Mr. Frumble gets wet.

These pupils are noisy.

Huckle is quiet.
He is reading.

Oops!
The bridge is too
narrow!
The car is too
wide!

Albert's barge goes slowly.

You need a bath!

clean pig   dirty pig

Roger's plane goes fast.

A wooden
stool
is hard.

A pillow is soft.

It's hot!

It's cold!

Huckle and Lowly are laughing.

Willy is crying.

Hey! Be a good sport!

Mr. Frumble came too early
to the dentist.
He must wait his turn.

Mr. Frumble was too late at the bus stop.

Now he must
wait for the
next bus.

Sophie is awake.

Arthur is
sleeping.

So please be quiet,
Sophie!